The Geology and Landscape of South West England

by Robert Westwood

Cornwall Devon Dorset Somerse

Inspiring Places Publishing
2 Down Lodge Close
Alderholt
Fordingbridge
SP6 3JA

ISBN 978-0-9928073-5-1

Inspiring places

Contents

Becky Falls, Devon.

Fold in cliffs, Watchet, Somerset.

Contents

Whale Rock, Bude, Cornwall.

Peveril Point, Swanage, Dorset.

Geological Map of South West England

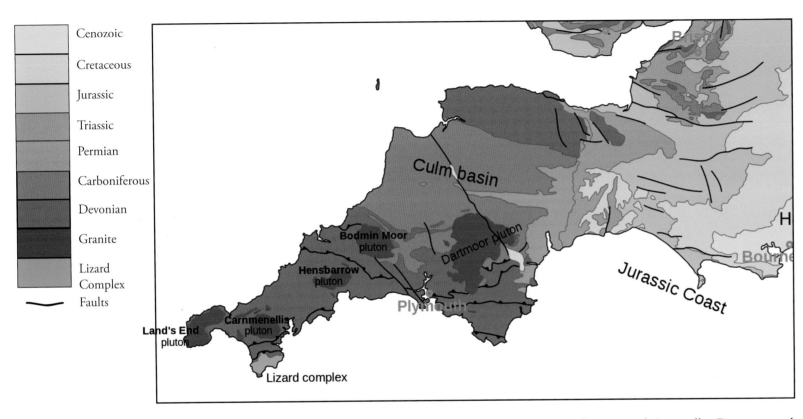

Above is a rough map of the bedrock geology of South West England. Much of Devon and Cornwall is Devonian and Carboniferous in age and the fact that the younger Carboniferous lies sandwiched between the Devonian is explained by a broad east-west trending synclinal fold with the Devonian lying underneath the Carboniferous. Younger rocks from the Permian onwards have partly covered this from the east. (Map courtesy Woudloper.)

The Geological Time Scale

The Earth is around four and a half billion years old and most of its geological history is referred to as the Precambrian. The Cambrian Period is the earliest time when easily recognisable fossils with hard parts appear in the rocks, thanks to what has been termed the "Cambrian explosion" - the seemingly sudden appearance of a multitude of life forms. The most familiar unit of geological time is the period and the boundaries between these are based on major changes in the fossil record. The boundaries of the eras represent even bigger changes, for example the mass extinctions at the end of the Upper Palaeozoic and the Mesozoic eras.

     Fossils can only date rocks relatively, it is left to radio-isotope dating to give us the absolute ages of rock strata. The fact that most of the rocks we see were formed relatively recently compared to the age of the Earth reflects the constant recycling produced by plate tectonics.

Era	Period	Age my
Quaternary →		2.3
Cenozoic	Neogene	23
	Palaeogene	
		65
Mesozoic	Cretaceous	
		145
	Jurassic	
		199
	Triassic	
		251
Upper Palaeozoic	Permian	
		299
	Carboniferous	
		359
	Devonian	
		416
Lower Palaeozoic	Silurian	443
	Ordovician	
		488
	Cambrian	
		542

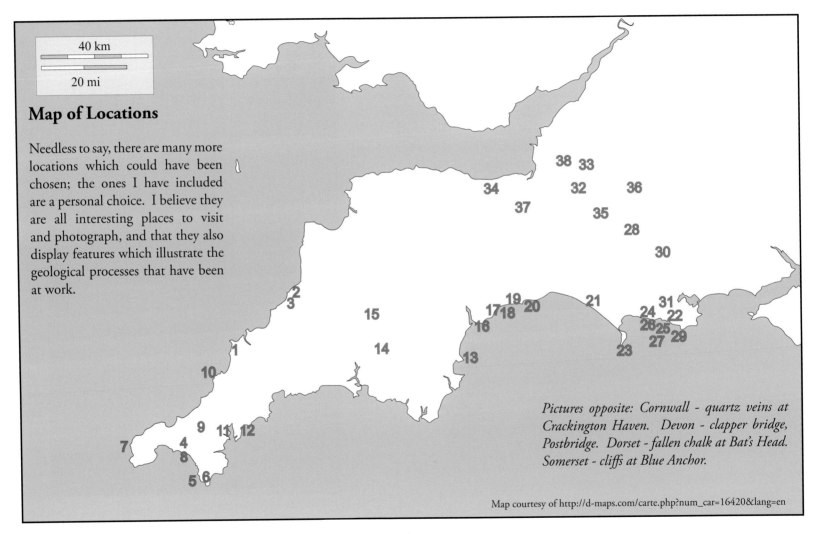

Map of Locations

Needless to say, there are many more locations which could have been chosen; the ones I have included are a personal choice. I believe they are all interesting places to visit and photograph, and that they also display features which illustrate the geological processes that have been at work.

40 km

20 mi

Pictures opposite: Cornwall - quartz veins at Crackington Haven. Devon - clapper bridge, Postbridge. Dorset - fallen chalk at Bat's Head. Somerset - cliffs at Blue Anchor.

Map courtesy of http://d-maps.com/carte.php?num_car=16420&lang=en

Location Key

Cornwall

1. Treyarnon
2. Crackington Haven
3. Millook Haven
4. Rinsey Head
5. Kynance Cove
6. Kennack Sands
7. Botallack
8. Trewavas Head
9. Carn Brea
10. St Agnes
11. Restronguet Creek
12. Pendower Beach

Devon

13. Triangle Point, and Hope's Nose
14. Sharpitor
15. Lydford Gorge
16. Orcombe Point
17. Budleigh Salterton
18. Ladram Bay
19. Hooken Cliff

Dorset

20. Monmouth Beach
21. West Bay
22. Clavell's Hard
23. Portland Bill
24. White Nothe
25. Lulworth Cove
26. Durdle Door
27. Man O' War Bay
28. Sherborne Abbey
29. Houns-tout
30. Hambledon Hill
31. Corfe Castle

Somerset

32. Glastonbury Tor
33. Ebbor Gorge
34. Watchet
35. Cadbury Castle
36. Vallis Vale
37. Cothelstone Hill
38. Cheddar Gorge

Introduction

Diverse and beautiful scenery is a defining feature of the south west of England. The South West Coast Path meanders over cliffs of gleaming chalk, bright red sandstone and tortured slate, while inland there are rolling hills, broad vales and dramatic moorland. Millions of visitors are drawn by this beauty every year, beauty that has evolved over millions of years through a multitude of processes. In my opinion a little knowledge of these processes can greatly enhance the enjoyment and appreciation of this wonderful landscape. Geology is a subject with a vast and complicated terminology but being able to recite and remember long names is not a prerequisite of real understanding. The aim of this book is to celebrate the landscape of South West England while providing some explanation of the processes that have formed it. The clues to help us decipher the geological history are everywhere and vary in scale from tiny veins in cliffs a few centimetres long to features stretching for several kilometres. They provide a fascinating insight into landscape evolution.

The crust of the Earth is often compared to the skin of an apple. While this may give some idea of the relative thickness of our planet's outer layer it is not representative of its nature. The Earth's crust is moving and changing all the time; from the perspective of our short lifespans it may appear that the hills and dales are eternal but on the geological time scale they are ephemeral. Movement and change require energy and the hot interior of the Earth has plenty.

Main picture: Granite cliffs at Trewavas Head on the south Cornish coast. Note the vertical and horizontal joints in the granite. These play a big part in the weathering process and are caused by the release of stresses as the granite cooled and material above it was eroded.

Far left: Steeply dipping Jurassic sediments on the beach at Watchet, Somerset.

Left: Chalk cliffs at Bat's Head, Dorset.

The heat is largely the product of the decay of heavy radioactive elements and sets up huge convection currents within the mantle, the thick layer beneath the crust. This hot, pressurised environment kilometres beneath our feet is hard to imagine, and our perception of rock as hard and brittle is largely irrelevant here. Under the tremendous heat and pressure rock behaves in a more fluid manner, it melts, partially and wholly, it flows, rises and falls. A little way down into the mantle is a layer known as the asthenosphere where the temperature and pressure combine to give the rock a degree of plasticity. It may be this layer that allows continental crust above to "float" and move on it. It is these ideas we must start with and there is plenty of evidence for their effects in the South West. We will also look at the effects of processes and environments on the Earth's surface.

This book will look separately at the counties of Cornwall, Devon, Dorset and Somerset. While these artificially defined areas were not created because of their distinct geological history, they do offer a measure of convenience for our story; generally speaking, for example, the oldest rocks are in the west and the youngest in the east. In each county we will look at a number of locations and explore what their large and/or small scale features tell us about their formation.

Perhaps inevitably, many of the locations are coastal; that is where the rocks are usually best exposed, but the landscape features of our lovely countryside can tell us much about the geology too.

Finally we should note that the South West is home to two UNESCO World Heritage sites, the Jurassic Coast and Cornish Mining. Both owe their status, wholly or partly, to the underlying geology of their regions. It is also home to the English Riviera Global Geopark set up specifically to bring geological heritage to the attention of the general public, something I very much hope this book will do.

Main picture: A granite tor, Sharpitor, on the edge of Dartmoor. The granite cooled slowly underground, from a melt that crystallised at around 1200 degrees Celsius.

Far left: Kenidjack Valley near St Just, Cornwall, part of the Cornish Mining World Heritage Site.

Left: Winspit - an old quarry in the Portland Stone on the Jurassic Coast.

Cornwall

Cornwall's magnificent coastline has abundant evidence of the deep, large scale processes that go on within the Earth's crust and the mantle, the thick layer beneath. Anyone familiar with the county's rocky shoreline will have seen and probably clambered over outcrops of dark slate that poke through the sandy beaches in thin, steeply inclined or often vertical layers. In many places veins of tough, white quartz penetrate the slate in a variety of angles, making the three dimensional pattern they must make within the rock difficult to imagine. More occasionally one can see layers contorted into complex folded patterns, sometimes on the scale of a few centimetres but sometimes taking up a whole cliff face. Such features may also be familiar to anyone who has spent time walking in the mountains of the Alps, for they are features associated with the huge earth movements that compress and contort rocks of the crust into giant mountain chains. This is perhaps easy to appreciate in the Alps where occasionally recumbently folded layers can be seen across a whole mountainside from several kilometres away; in Cornwall's more gentle landscape perhaps not so easy. Yet Cornwall was once part of a great mountain chain every bit as spectacular as the Alps, the difference in the nature of their landscapes today is largely caused by time. Walk along Cornwall's rocky coastline and you are walking on the eroded core of an ancient mountain range.

These days it is a commonly accepted fact that mountains are formed when two plates of the Earth's crust collide and squeeze the layers of rock caught between them. The driving mechanism of this movement is still debated. Down the middle of most of the Earth's oceans are fissures above where hot plumes rise; here constant volcanic activity creates new oceanic crust and this may contribute to the plate movement. Many scientists now think that the drag caused by oceanic crust sinking at subduction zones is a major driving force. Current plate collision zones are marked by frequent volcanic activity and earthquakes, ancient collision zones often by old mountain chains.

There is much more to Cornwall's geology than slate, its rocks have been formed in a variety of environments. Its sediments have collected in deep ocean basins and others in shallow tropical seas, while its famous granite was forged in a fiery environment deep underground, allowing an extended period of cooling that ended with the formation of valuable mineral deposits injected into the surrounding rocks by residual fluids.

More recent processes have also helped shape Cornwall's scenery, once rocks have been uplifted above sea level the forces of erosion immediately begin their recycling work, breaking up the minerals and transporting them back to the sea ready to be incorporated in future sedimentary layers. The landscape is constantly changing and the more extreme conditions experienced by these islands in the last and relatively recent ice age have particularly left their mark.

Right: Cudden Point, Prussia Cove - metamorphosed igneous rocks.

Treyarnon ~ *slates*

Slate is a ubiquitous rock in all orogenic belts, areas of the crust where mountain chains have been formed by the collision of continental plates or the subduction of an oceanic plate under a continental one. It is formed by what is known as regional metamorphism, increased temperature and pressure experienced by vast volumes of the crust as the plates collide. The overall compositions of the rocks involved are not generally changed by this process, but over thousands, or even millions, of years the constituents may recrystallise into different minerals while still remaining solid. The crystals may also orientate themselves relative to the direction of the pressure, and this is the key feature of slates.

Slates have typically formed from shales or similar fine grained sediments with lots of clay minerals. Clays are hydrous aluminium silicates, and are a common product of weathering, particularly of the feldspars in igneous rocks. They form two dimensional, flat crystals which, as they recrystallise, orientate themselves at right angles to the direction of the pressure. It is this that gives slate its cleavage or preferred direction of splitting, as the flat crystals are aligned in primarily one direction. What better rock to appreciate the slow, inexorable processes that drive the rock cycle? Minerals solidified from a molten magma to form an igneous rock, are eventually exposed to the elements, weathered and carried to the sea where thousands of feet of fine grained sediment slowly collects. Their ocean is gradually squeezed out of existence as the continents collide and, by now deeply buried, the minerals are subjected to increased temperature and pressure. Recrystallised

into a slate they become part of a great mountain chain, uplifted as the collision progresses. The forces of erosion once more come into play and the mountains are worn down. On Cornwall's rugged coastline we now see these slates continuing to erode and weathered minerals once more slowly drift to the sea bed.

Main picture: Steeply dipping Devonian slates at Treyarnon.
Below: Colourful slate at Polzeath. Notice how the slaty cleavage runs almost horizontally across the picture whereas the coloured bands which show the original sedimentary layers are at an angle to this. This is because the original layers have been folded and so present at different angles while the cleavage is uniformly at right angles to the direction of compression.

Crackington Haven ~ *turbidites*

How many people stop to look at the surface of rock layers and ponder what processes caused the varied textures they see? The rocks of Crackington Haven and northwards along the Cornish coast are from the Upper Carboniferous, around 320 million years ago. At this time north Cornwall and much of Devon was part of a marine basin with mountains to the south and a great delta to the north where luxuriant forests would eventually form the Coal Measures. This basin had probably formed due to some stretching of the Earth's crust; although the structures of Cornwall's rocks are largely associated with compressional forces as two plates collided, in reality things are more complicated, for example, an oblique collision between two plates can result in part of the crust being stretched. Earthquakes associated with the collision frequently shook the sediment building up on the edge of the basin resulting in turbid flows tumbling towards the deeper middle. Coarse material like sand settled first followed by finer clays resulting in the alternating bands of sandstones and shales we see today on the coast at Crackington Haven. On the bedding surfaces there are often ripple and scour marks visible, formed by the detritus bowled along the sea bed by powerful currents. These layers are known as turbidites.

Quartz veins or sheets cut through the cracks and fissures of the stressed strata, forming complicated patterns. They can form in a number of ways; when igneous intrusions like the granites cool, superheated fluids flow along planes of weakness in the surrounding rocks and deposit minerals. Groundwater around such bodies can also be heated and circulate through the rocks, dissolving and precipitating minerals as it does so. Quartz veins can also form by a process known as lateral secretion, where rocks that are heated and subject to pressure secrete minerals, typically quartz, into existing cracks and joints. The quartz veins that pervade the rocks at Crackington Haven come under this category; the quartz has been "sweated" from the sandstones as they have suffered under the compression between two plates.

Main picture: Scour marks left by ancient turbidity currents. They have been filled with sediment and subsequent folding has left them upside down.

Below: Many quartz veins are visible in the steeply dipping layers.

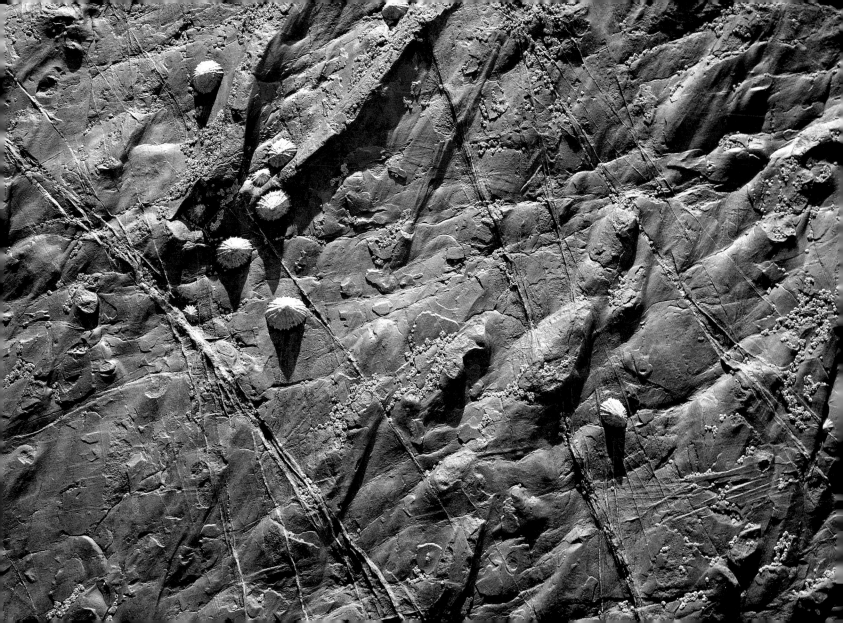

Millook Haven ~ *chevron folds*

It is the layering in rocks that usually makes the fact that they have been folded apparent. Most sediments, and some volcanic rocks, are deposited in horizontal layers, often on the sea floor or in lakes. A change in the environment can lead to a change in the nature of the sediment deposited and hence a recognisably different layer. Folding of the layers in rocks is usually the result of compressional forces caused by plate tectonics. Tightly folded layers show that these forces have shortened parts of the Earth's crust by a considerable extent – what we would expect when two plates collide.

We all know that on the surface of the Earth rocks behave in a brittle manner when subject to stress; they fracture and break. However, below about fifteen kilometres down in the crust the increased pressure and temperature cause rock to deform in a more ductile manner under stress; they can flow and bend without fracturing. How they do so can be seen by the folded layers presented by many sedimentary rocks that have been caught up in such earth movements. These deformations do not happen at a rate observable on a human timescale but over hundreds and thousands of years. Sophisticated instruments record that plates typically move a few centimetres each year.

The type of folding visible in rocks is a product of the forces involved and the nature of the rock. Dramatic chevron folds such as those seen at Millook Haven can be created when sediments with alternating layers of hard and soft rock, and of a certain thickness, are compressed. Here the hard turbidite sandstones with the softer layers of shale in between have provided just the right materials for the chevron folds to form.

Main picture: The wonderful chevron folds in the cliffs at Millook Haven. Note the alternating layers perfect for the production of these folds. It is estimated that this folding represents a shortening of the crust by as much as sixty per cent.

Far left: Small scale folding in the slates at Boscastle. Here we can see that the cleavage has itself been folded. This means that there was a secondary deformation or compression after the original which formed the cleavage. It is quite common to be able to recognise several episodes of deformation in these rocks.

Left: More small scale folding in slates at Porthleven. The situation here is complex with three separate phases of folding having been recognised.

Rinsey Head ~ *what is granite?*

Granite is an igneous rock that cooled from a molten state; its texture of interlocking crystals of varying sizes indicating that the original liquid was a mixture of many elements that formed different minerals at different temperatures as the melt cooled. The fact that the crystals are relatively large tells us that it also cooled very slowly and therefore very deeply over hundreds, if not thousands of years.

The composition of granite is representative of what is called the "continental crust". The Earth's crust is divided into two parts, the other being the "oceanic crust". Continental crust is less dense and much thicker than oceanic crust and, as the name suggests, forms most of the planet's landmasses. Its chief elements are oxygen, silicon and aluminium and these are the main components of the minerals in granite, together with calcium, sodium and potassium. All granite and continental crust has been

formed as a consequence of collisions between the plates of the Earth's crust, particularly those where an oceanic plate is forced down under a continental plate (subducted).

Oceanic crust has more minerals containing iron and magnesium than continental crust and is also less rich in silica. When it is melted and begins to cool some feldspars, plus minerals rich in iron and magnesium and relatively deficient in silica will crystallise out first, meaning the remaining liquid is rich in silica. This "fractional crystallisation" is the process which leads to the formation of a liquid which eventually cools to form granite and hence to all of the Earth's continental crust and the land on which we live. When you look closely at a piece of granite notice the colourless or white crystalline quartz which forms the matrix in which the other minerals sit. This is the result of it being the last mineral to crystallise. This also explains the very many quartz veins we see cutting through the slates which often border the granite (see also pages 16 and 30).

Main picture: The granite cliffs of Rinsey Head. The building was once the "count house" or head office of the mine that operated here. Left: Granite boulders at Porthgwarra; note the large feldspar crystals which crystallised first from the melt. Feldspar refers to a group of minerals which are aluminium silicates with sodium, potassium and calcium in varying proportions. Together they make up well over fifty per cent of the Earth's crust. The name feldspar means 'field mineral or rock', so called because it is so common.

Kynance Cove ~ *rocks from the mantle*

The rocks of the Lizard Peninsula were an enigma to early geologists. It was always clear that they were very different from the rocks of the rest of Cornwall and it is now known that they represent a rare and somewhat exotic geological event.

The Lizard rocks form what is known as an "ophiolite complex" and were originally a slice of oceanic crust and part of the mantle beneath, which became caught up in the collision of plates during the Devonian Period and pushed up into the continental crust above. The serpentine which we see at Kynance Cove was once a dark, relatively dense rock called peridotite and was originally part of the upper mantle. It has been metamorphosed to serpentine, so called because its multicoloured appearance resembles a snake skin. Chemically there is little difference between the two rocks, apart from the introduction of water, thought to have percolated down as the plates collided, and the heat and pressure it was subjected to have led to a rearrangement of the elements to form the mineral serpentine.

This slab of oceanic crust and mantle is thought to have been thrust up from the south as the plate collision caused the Rheic Ocean* to close. The line of this thrust can still be seen today; it stretches from Porthallow on the east side of the Lizard to Polurrian Cove on the west. To the north of this divide the rocks are completely different, the mainly Devonian sediments we see elsewhere in Cornwall.

* The Rheic Ocean began around 540 million years ago as several smaller continents drifted northwards from the large southern continent known as Gondwana.

Main picture: Kynance Cove has been carved from two types of serpentine, bastite and tremolite; the names refer to minerals formed by the alteration of the original rock minerals.

Far left: Serpentine pebbles on the beach at Kynance.

Left: Two small faults are apparent on the beach at Kynance.

Kennack Sands ~ *an igneous complex*

You don't need to be a geologist to recognise that the rocks in and around Kennack Sands tell a complicated story. In many places they look "mixed up" and this is perhaps a pertinent description. Their history is still part of our story of orogenesis or mountain building and the collision of plates. We have seen how the Lizard Peninsula represents an interesting twist in this story when a piece of oceanic crust and some of the layer beneath, the mantle, became caught up in the plate movement and was obducted or pushed up towards the surface. As this happened heat was also transferred upwards causing rocks to wholly or partially melt.

This leads us to the rocks of Kennack Sands which are a mixture of igneous rocks intruded into the neighbouring rocks of the Lizard around 370-380 million years ago. Shortly after this they were metamorphosed by the continuing heat and pressure. It is thought that the melting or partial melting took place at the base of the slice of mantle as it was being thrust upwards, forming new igneous rocks which mixed and mingled with each other. The evidence for this mixing is everywhere at Kennack Sands. Dykes are sheets of igneous rock injected into surrounding rocks and are quite easy to pick out at Kennack Sands.

Main picture: Cliffs at Kennack Sands. Note the dyke of igneous rock running at an angle of about 45 degrees through the cliff face, starting just above the beach on the left hand side. This is a "basic" igneous rock, meaning its composition is relatively low in silica.

Far left: Another "basic" dyke in close up. Note the edges of the dyke where the rock it was intruded into has been altered somewhat by contact with the hot, molten magma.

Left: Detail in the Kennack Gneiss. This is a highly metamorphosed rock and partially melted by the extreme heat. Different parts have become mixed up while in a fluid, plastic state.

The Cornish Mining World Heritage Site

From the beginning of the eighteenth century to the end of the nineteenth the mining industry of Cornwall and west Devon played a vital role in Britain's economic and industrial growth. The main products were ores of copper and tin, but others such as lead and zinc were also extracted. Arsenic was often a valuable by-product of the refining process. All these useful minerals were formed naturally by processes associated with the emplacement of the granite batholith that lies under South West England and the centres of the mining industry were all on or around the various outcrops of the granite. The World Heritage Site, founded in July 2006, comprises ten distinct areas, nine in Cornwall and one in Devon. All have a distinctive character and the effects of the mining industry on the landscape are obvious. The next two articles explore the processes that formed and concentrated the minerals.

Carn Brea (main picture) is an isolated granite hill between Redruth and Camborne and was once at the centre of the Cornish mining industry. The granite is connected to the Carnmenellis granite to the east and both are associated with rich veins or lodes containing copper, tin, lead, tungsten and other valuable minerals. Scattered all around it are the ruins of old engine houses and filled in mine shafts. To the south of the hill in particular are the ruins of many mines which once worked The Great Flat Lode. This was a particularly rich and relatively thick lode which unusually had a fairly shallow dip and so could be followed easily across the landscape without the need for deep mines.

Main picture: The summit of Carn Brea with the town of Redruth in the background.
Far left: To the south of Carn Brea the landscape is dotted with ruined engine houses that once served the mines working the Great Flat Lode.
Left: "Man made" rock in a wall in Hayle. This is scoria, the slag remaining after the smelting of tin ore.

The Crown Mines, Botallack ~ *mineral wealth*

Cornwall's mining industry has a long history stretching back to ancient times, with the ores of tin and copper the main products. It is well known that these ore deposits are associated with the granite outcrops, particularly around their edges, but why is this so, what created these valuable mineral resources?

As we have seen, granite is an igneous rock that cooled slowly from a molten state, with different minerals precipitating out at different temperatures as the melt cooled. For those with a little knowledge of chemistry it should come as no surprise that those elements higher up the reaction series started to form compounds and crystallise out first. Thus it is that we often see large feldspar crystals, which are silicates of sodium, potassium, calcium and aluminium, that have had time to grow in an otherwise still liquid mix. Towards the end of the process any excess silica that has not been used will crystallise as quartz, filling in the spaces around the other crystals. Also left unattached towards the end will be those elements that are fairly unreactive, particularly copper and tin. These will circulate around the still hot granite in superheated water that has percolated down. This will penetrate into joints, fissures and any planes of weakness in the surrounding rocks. The cooling and loss of pressure will lead to the fluid solidifying, mostly to veins of quartz which are ubiquitous in the sediments surrounding granite masses. Where the fluids are relatively rich in other minerals, valuable mineral lodes may be formed. These lodes often form along cleavage planes in the surrounding slate which means they usually extend in a vertical or near vertical plane – hence the need for mines to extend downwards in order to follow the mineral deposits. As technology improved so mines were able to go deeper and deeper, and in some cases this meant following the lodes out under the sea.

The Crown Mines at Botallack were among the most profitable in Cornwall. In the 1840s when it was thought the mines had largely been exhausted, new discoveries of mineral lodes and the arrival of steam engines meant it was possible to extend the workings downwards and under the sea. Production of tin reached a peak in the 1860s when the mines employed over five hundred people and used eleven steam engines. They reached about four hundred metres out to sea and around five hundred metres below sea level.

Main picture: The Crown Mines at Botallack.

Left: Mine waste, the colours betray the presence of iron and copper.

St Agnes ~ *tin streaming*

Alluvial tin has been mined in Cornwall for over two thousand years, long before the technology existed to drive mines deep underground. The formation of alluvial or "placer" tin deposits is quite straightforward in principle. As the rocks including mineral lodes were eroded, the detritus was carried away by fast streams coming off the granite uplands and deposited further downstream on floodplains or where the gradient decreased. Cassiterite, the main mineral of tin, is about two and a half times heavier than the other weathered material which is "sorted" by the river or stream and carried further. Thus tin rich sediment accumulates at certain locations. Most such deposits in Cornwall have been all but exhausted by centuries of working; the water of the stream was passed over the alluvium and it was relatively easy to wash away the lighter material leaving the valuable tin ore behind.

The formation of these placer deposits has undoubtedly been helped by the changes in sea level the South West experienced throughout the Ice Age. A fall in sea level resulted in the "rejuvenation" of rivers and consequently increased erosional power. A rise in sea level had the opposite effect and resulted in rivers being unable to carry so much load and forming alluvial deposits. A number of the rivers draining into the estuary of the River Fal carried tin rich sediment and the Carnon Stream Mine in Restronguet Creek (see page 34) was one of the most important, with shafts extending out under the water.

The Blue Hills Tin Mine near St Agnes mined alluvial tin from the floor of Trevellas Coombe and from the beaches where it had been thrown up by wave action.

Main picture: Trevellas Coombe between St Agnes and Perranporth. Alluvial tin was gathered from this stream for many centuries.

Left: Cligga Head on the cliffs north of St Agnes. This rock is known as greisen and is formed by the alteration of granite by residual fluids which are forced into spaces between crystals. This process also tends to concentrate elements such as tin, tungsten and sometimes copper. Here at St Agnes and nearby Perranporth such greisen veins were important mineral veins. These altered greisens are more easily weathered than the original granites and it is the erosion of rocks like these that has led to the economically important alluvial or placer deposits. In some areas streams were actually diverted to flow over such rocks so as to facilitate the formation of alluvial ore deposits.

Trewavas Head ~ *aplite sills*

Look east from the cliffs of Trewavas Head and you will see Megiliggar Rocks. At Trewavas you are standing on the eastern section of the Tregonning Granite, but at Megiliggar the cliffs are clearly made of slate, apart from some interesting exceptions. The junction between the granite and the slate here is almost vertical and is a faulted junction. Easily picked out in the cliffs, even from Trewavas, are several light coloured sills, almost horizontal. Sills are sheet-like igneous intrusions that have been injected concordantly to the prevailing planes of weakness, bedding planes of sedimentary rocks or, as in this case, the cleavage planes of the slate.

The sills at Megiliggar were among the last products of the igneous activity associated with the Tregonning Granite and represent the concentration of volatile constituents under the roof of impermeable slate which had already been baked and contorted by the intrusion of the main body of granite. The sills are composed of aplite, a fine grained rock that consists mainly of quartz and alkali feldspar, which is feldspar that is rich in sodium or potassium. These would be the final crystallisation products of the granite magma and the rock is fine grained because it cooled quickly.

The granite is thought to have been emplaced by a process known as "stoping". As the surrounding "country rock" is heated by the molten granite it expands and fractures causing blocks to break off and sink through the magma, allowing it to gradually ascend. The fractures may simply fill with magma forming features such as the sills we see at Megiliggar.

The two engine houses at Trewavas Head were once part of the Wheal Trewavas Mine that worked copper lodes extending out under the sea. They were quite profitable for a short while in the mid-nineteenth century.

Main picture: From Trewavas Head the aplite sills are clearly visible in the cliffs opposite.

Left: Ruined engine houses at Trewavas Head.

Restronguet Creek ~ *a rise in sea level*

Large changes in sea level can seem difficult to understand; most of Britain, after all, is covered by sedimentary rocks deposited in oceans – how is it that places once several hundred metres below the waves are now well above mean sea level? Most such changes in the distribution of land and sea are tectonic, that is they were caused by the movement of the plates of the Earth's crust and the gradual formation of continental crust. However, there are other factors that affect sea level; a rise in global temperatures causes the oceans to expand and so raise the average sea level. Glacial periods trap water on land as ice, lowering the sea level which rises again as the ice melts.

South West England shows much evidence of sea level

changes with a variety of causes. The main phase of the Alpine mountain building episode around fifteen to twenty million years ago resulted in significant sea level changes as the crust buckled, sank and bounced back. At one point the sea level was some 120 metres above today's level and the flat interior of the Lizard Peninsula was formed by wave erosion at this time. Similar wave cut platforms from this period can be seen elsewhere in Cornwall. Subsequent falls in sea level led to river valleys being "rejuvenated" or more deeply incised by rivers given extra power by an increase in gradient.

The latest change in sea level and the one that has left the most obvious features is the rise following the last glacial period about ten thousand years ago when the great ice sheets that covered most of Britain melted. Many river valleys, particularly those that emptied into the English Channel, were flooded, resulting in the wonderful long twisting estuaries known as rias. They are often fed by relatively insignificant rivers but provide wonderful, deep harbours for a variety of craft.

Main picture: Restronguet Creek is an example of a ria or drowned river valley and originally held a tributary of the River Fal. The once important mining port of Devoran is a little way upstream from here.

Left: A view over Kynance Cove on the Lizard Peninsula; the flat inland surface is an ancient wave cut platform formed when the sea level was much higher than it is today.

Pendower Beach ~ *more sea level changes*

We have seen that Cornwall's coast bears much evidence of changes in sea level; the most conspicuous features being the drowned valleys or rias of rivers like the Helford and Fal. Elsewhere are landforms created when the sea level was higher such as the flat, erosional surface particularly noticeable on the Lizard.

Many of these features are a product of the last ice age and its cycle of glacial and interglacial periods. Technically we are still in an ice age that began around 2.6 million years ago, since the earth still has large ice sheets covering the poles; for much of its history this has not been the case. We are, however, in a warmer interglacial period with the last glacial epoch ending around 10 000 years ago. During this last Ice Age the sea level has fluctuated as the amount of water trapped in ice sheets has varied.

Pendower Beach on the Roseland Peninsula has a very good example of a raised beach. On top of contorted, steeply dipping Devonian slates lies a horizontal layer of conglomerate, a weakly bound mixture of sand and pebbles that once lay on an ancient beach. This is less than 2 million years old and formed when the sea level was a few metres higher than it is today and eroded the old landscape of slate. This results in a feature known as an unconformity, two rock layers in juxtaposition with a large time gap between their formation – in this case well over 300 million years.

While the ice sheets of the glacial periods never reached as far as Cornwall, the South West would have been subject to periglacial conditions where repeated freeze-thaw cycles resulted in the weathering of rocks into angular pieces. Large scale movements of this detritus on permanently frozen subsoil resulted in the deposition of what is known as glacial "head", something that can be seen in many places in Cornwall.

Main picture: The raised beach and unconformity at Pendower Beach. The horizontal line of the unconformity is clearly visible about two thirds of the way up from the bottom of the photograph.

Left: Porth Nanven near St Just - the rounded boulders in the cliff are part of a storm beach formed when the sea level was higher, while above is glacial head, its angular pebbles and boulders indicating they have not been worn by wave action like those in the raised beach just below.

The Variscan Orogeny

An orogeny is a mountain building episode caused by the coming together of two crustal plates. This could be where thinner oceanic crust is subducted or pushed under thicker continental crust, or it could be the result of two continental plates colliding. In either case we would expect to see deformation or folding of rocks, metamorphic and igneous rocks. Mountain chains like the Himalayas, Alps and Rockies are the product of relatively recent plate collisions while the contorted rocks of older ranges that have undergone millions of years of erosion sit like scar tissue on the face of the Earth.

The Variscan Orogeny occurred when a large continent named Gondwana (modern South America, Africa, India, Australasia and Antarctica) moved northwards and collided with Laurussia (North America, Europe and Asia). This collision would eventually form the supercontinent of Pangaea comprising all of the Earth's landmass. Caught in the middle of this collision, Cornwall and much of Devon were part of a marine trough called the North Variscan Foredeep, extending from western Ireland to Poland. As mountains gradually rose to the south of this rivers poured eroded sediment into the trough. In the final stages of the collision, during the late Carboniferous Period, the trough was compressed and the sediments folded into new mountains. Also at this time the huge granite batholith was emplaced under the mountain chain.

The orogeny had taken place over many millions of years and the rocks of Cornwall now represent the eroded core of these once mighty mountains. Once this is realised, many of the features we see in the rocks fit in with this complex story. As two continental landmasses collide the crust between is shortened. The layers of rock must accommodate this and do so either by folding or by fracturing, with layers being thrust over the top of other layers. Intense folding of strata and thrust faults are seen all over Cornwall, sometimes these are large scale features, at other times small scale. It is fascinating to pick out small, convoluted folds and tiny thrusts in the cliffs.

Main picture: These steeply inclined strata at Millook Haven have been intensely folded during the Variscan Orogeny.
Below: Small scale folds and thrusts are visible in these slates at Boscastle.

Devon

Devon is unique among English counties in that it has a geological period named after it. The Devonian is so called because Devon was the first place it was extensively studied. These rocks are the oldest in the county and date from between around 416 to 360 million years old. Elsewhere in Britain Devonian rocks are mainly what is called the Old Red Sandstone, desert deposits formed in hot, arid conditions, whereas in Devon they are typical marine sediments. At the time Britain was near the Equator in the collision zone of two crustal plates, a collision that would eventually form the Variscan mountain chain of which Cornwall and Devon were a part. Most of Britain was land and the Old Red Sandstone represents the sediment washed from mountains, formed by an earlier orogeny, onto the plains and basins beneath. However, South West England was still covered by sea and the

marine Devonian sediments here were also made from detritus washed from the mountains to the north. This situation continued into the Carboniferous although by then the sea had returned to cover much of Britain.

As the geological map of the county shows, the Devonian rocks lie to the north and south of Devon, with the younger Carboniferous in the middle. This represents a very broad synclinal structure or fold and it is perhaps easy to appreciate that the collision of the plates was along an east-west axis. The formation of the huge granite batholith which underlies much of South West England occurred towards the end of the Carboniferous and the beginning of the Permian, in the final throes of the mountain building episode. In Dartmoor, Devon has the largest exposure of this.

In the east of the county it can be seen that the sediments from the Permian and Mesozoic Era cut across the east-west alignment of the older sediments. Those from the Permian and Triassic periods are again largely desert sandstones formed from the weathering of the vast supercontinent of Pangaea which had been created by a number of plate collisions.

Main picture: The Bronze Age stone rows at Merrivale on Dartmoor. At this time the granite uplands were much more hospitable places thanks to a warmer and drier climate.
Left: Becky Falls, one of Dartmoor's pretty waterfalls formed as rivers flow off the hard granite onto softer sedimentary rocks.

The English Riviera Geopark

The European Geopark Network was set up in 2000 and at the time of writing comprises sixty-nine sites, including six in the UK. One of its main aims was to promote geological heritage to the general public, primarily through the development of geological tourism. There are now over one hundred such sites world-wide recognised by UNESCO. The English Riviera Geopark was created in 2007 and based around the international importance of thirty-two locations around the site. The oldest rocks here are marine Devonian sediments that were folded and metamorphosed in the Variscan Orogeny. At places these are overlain by Permian conglomerates and sandstones laid down in desert conditions and

weathered from the mountains formed by the orogeny. At Kents Cavern there are important Quaternary features that provide much information about the environment and fauna of the Ice Age.

Hope's Nose is a small peninsula that has good exposures of the Devonian Daddyhole Limestone. On the southern tip is an impressive structural feature – an overturned or recumbent fold in the thinly bedded limestones with underneath a low angle thrust fault. Both these are typical of the intense deformation in a fold mountain belt. If you imagine the fold in three dimensions, the axis of the fold is a line running along the tip of the curvature (at right angles to the page). This trends roughly east-west, suggesting a compression in a north-south direction. Additionally, it may perhaps seem clear that the "push" was from south to north (south is to right of page). The orientation of other such folds from this time over South West England confirms this general picture.

Main picture: The recumbent fold in the Daddyhole Limestone at Hope's Nose. The thrust can be seen just a little way up from the bottom of the photograph running almost horizontally.

Left: The Daddyhole Limestone at Triangle Point (see page 44). Somewhat complicated by faults, the strata seem to be dipping steeply to the left of the photograph. In fact these layers are inverted and represent the bottom limb of another recumbent fold.

Triangle Point, Torbay ~ *tropical Devonian seas*

Much of what is now Britain was land during the Devonian Period, an arid landscape where the Caledonian mountains were being quickly eroded by seasonal rivers. At the start of the period plant life was beginning to colonise the continents, but the early varieties had no roots and provided little protection against erosion. This was the environment in which the Old Red Sandstone was deposited, from South Wales to the far north-east of Scotland. The famous Old Man of Hoy has been sculpted from this rock, in this case a fluvial sandstone. In other places the sandstone is formed from wind blown desert sands or temporary "playa" lakes.

We have seen, however, that not all of Britain was above sea level. The South West was covered by the Rheic Ocean (see page 22) that was being squeezed as the continents of Gondwana and Laurussia drew closer together. Across much of Cornwall we see Devonian slates formed from fine grained relatively deep sea sediments, but here in South Devon the situation was different. The limestones of the Torbay area indicate a shallower sea, probably on a continental shelf and perhaps close to land. The fossil corals in the limestones confirm this; corals live in warm, shallow waters where there is sunlight and an abundance of life. Volcanic islands occasionally rose from the waters adding layers of ash to the sediments.

Just like the fine grained silts and clays that were baked and compressed into slate, the limestones here show signs of having been folded and contorted by these great earth movements. Small faults and thrusts are everywhere and sometimes the strata follow graceful curves. At Triangle Point the limestone layers are upside down; they are part of a great recumbent fold (see page 42). There are a number of indications that tell us this, one of them being the way sediment has filled the fossil shells that are abundant in these rocks.

Main picture: Two aspects of Devonian limestone; on the top the rock is full of fossil gastropods and brachiopods, on the bottom fossil corals. Left: A fine example of a fault at Triangle Point. The grey rock to the right has slipped down obliquely relative to the pink rock.

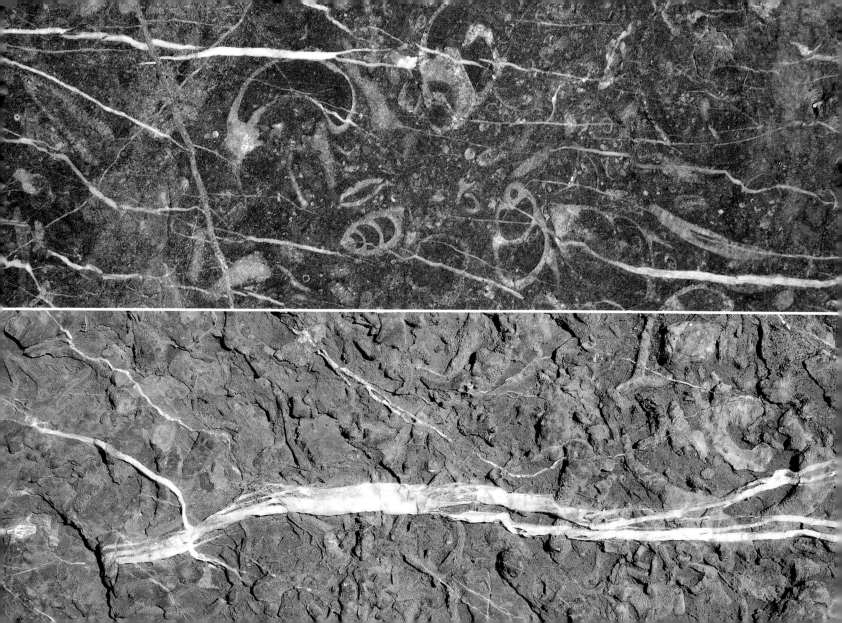

Sharpitor ~ *granite tors*

The huge granite batholith under South West England was emplaced around 290 to 280 million years ago. It took a long time to cool and as it did so contraction caused the formation of mainly vertical joints. The overlying cover of sedimentary rocks, around two to three kilometres thick, was eroded fairly quickly, allowing the granite to expand upwards and leading to the formation of largely horizontal joints. These joints have been an important factor in the erosion of the granite.

Chemical weathering has also played a leading part in the formation of the tors. Hot fluids circulating around the granite led to the decomposition of some of the feldspar to kaolin, a soft, white clay mineral. Then, following the Cretaceous Period, a hot,

wet, tropical climate facilitated the further chemical weathering of the feldspars, particularly along the joints. The landscape was thickly covered by vegetation and groundwater made acidic by rotting plants is very reactive. The granite was both softened and weakened by these processes.

Joints in the granite continued to be an important factor in its erosion during the Ice Age. As water in the joints froze it expanded and forced the joints apart. A freeze – thaw cycle resulted in the granite being broken up by repeated expansions. The broken pieces moved downhill under gravity, helped by a process known as solifluction, a slow downslope movement of waterlogged detritus due to repeated freezing and thawing. During the summer months the top layers of soil would become a soggy mess, strewn with boulders and smaller rocks from the broken up granite. This would slide easily over the still frozen sub-soil. Hence today we are left with jointed and weathered granite tors, surrounded by extensive fields of frost shattered rocks.

Main picture: Sharpitor on Dartmoor, one of the many granite tors in this dramatic landscape. Note the extent of the boulders and "clitter field", frost shattered rocks that have moved downwards under gravity and via solifluction.

Left: Grimspound Bronze Age settlement on Dartmoor provides a reminder of climate change. During the Bronze Age the climate was warmer than it is today and the moor was quite heavily populated and cultivated. On the hill in the distance is another tor.

Lydford Gorge ~ *river capture*

Dartmoor's rivers are famous for their beauty and diversity. The radial pattern of drainage on and around the moor was established once the granite had been exposed by the erosion of the overlying sediment. Since we find bits of eroded granite in the New Red Sandstone of the Permian and Triassic periods, it must have happened before then. Although the broad pattern was established long ago, the present nature of the rivers owes much to the last few hundred thousand years and the effects of the Ice Age.

When the rivers leave the moor and the granite they encounter softer rocks, usually slates, so it is no surprise to find waterfalls, cataracts and gorges on the fringes of Dartmoor. Lydford Gorge is the deepest in South West England and owes its character not just to the softer Devonian slates here but to the fact that it has "captured" the waters of another river. Once much shorter, the head of the River Lyd eroded back until it intersected with the River Burn, which was then diverted into the channel of the Lyd. The increase in gradient experienced by the waters of what was the River Burn eroded the deep gorge we see today. The "elbow of capture" is marked by the White Lady Falls.

The slates of Lydford Gorge are also of interest. They are Devonian in age, originally fine grained sediments, but metamorphosed to slate by the Variscan Orogeny. Within the gorge are two important thrusts, low angle shears in the rock where one block of crust has been pushed or thrust over another by the collision of plates. Such features are relatively common in mountain ranges and are one of the ways in which the crust is shortened when caught between colliding plates. In places you can see minor folds in the slates, indicative of the contortions they have been put through.

Main picture: The River Lyd in Lydford Gorge.

Far left: White Lady Falls.

Left: The River Lyd flowing over steeply dipping Devonian slates.

Orcombe Point ~ *start of the Jurassic Coast*

The coast of east Devon is famous for its striking red cliffs. These are clearly sandstones, the red colour coming from the oxidation of iron which often acts as a cement binding the grains together. The grains are mostly quartz and other more resistant minerals largely unaltered chemically by the weathering of the rocks they were originally a part of. The sandstones are of continental origin, that is they were laid down not in the sea but on land, most of them by rivers and lakes in an arid, desert landscape. As we might expect there are also wind blown deposits, ancient desert sand dunes. Many of these rocks were deposited in seasonal "playa" lakes that dried out in summer and where perhaps flash floods occasionally brought much detritus from mountains nearby.

In east Devon these sandstones are largely of Triassic age; west of the Exe Estuary they are Permian. By the end of the Permian the movement of plates had brought all of the Earth's landmass together in one giant supercontinent named Pangaea. The ocean into which Cornwall's and Devon's sediments had been dropped had closed up and new mountains formed. Most of this vast expanse was arid desert.

One clue to the origin of these red rocks is commonly seen in the cliffs, current bedding. As the name implies it is a feature brought about by the work of currents. When they reach a plain and their gradient drops, rivers begin to meander; over time their course changes, back and forth across the valley or flood plain. In the sediments that have formed this way layers of sand can be seen cutting across one another reflecting the changing course of the river. This can clearly be seen in the small photograph. Look out too for changes in the layers of the sandstones, bands with lots of pebbles may indicate formation in a river delta or there may be layers of mudstone where, perhaps, finer material has been carried out to the centre of a large lake. All such changes reflect a change in the environment of deposition.

Main picture: The red sandstone cliffs near Orcombe Point, the start of the Jurassic Coast. Note there appears to be a near-vertical fault in the sandstones in the middle of the picture.
Left: A close up of current bedding in a Triassic sandstone caused by the meandering of an ancient, seasonal river. Such bedding can also be a product of aeolian or wind deposition.

Budleigh Salterton ~ *the Pebble Bed*

———————

Geological strata are often named after the places where they are first extensively studied or where they present the most complete and accessible outcrop. The Kimmeridge Clay is one such layer and another, equally well known amongst geologists, is the Budleigh Salterton Pebble Bed. Unsurprisingly most of the pebbles along Budeigh Salterton's beach come from this stratum, but they are also found at many places along the south coast, swept there by longshore drift driven by the prevailing westerly winds.

The Pebble Bed can be seen at the bottom of the cliffs to the west of the beach. At the beginning of the cliff the junction with the overlying Otter Sandstone is clear, both dipping gently eastwards. The pebbles are mostly quartzite, a hard sandstone metamorphosed when it was caught up in a mountain building episode. Radio-

isotope dating has put the formation of the quartzite around 440 million years ago, a good 200 million years before the Pebble Bed came into being. The size of the pebbles tells us they were deposited by a fast flowing river which it is believed originated in mountains in what is now Brittany. The northward flow of the river is indicated by the fact that the size of the pebbles decreases northwards and by the occurrence of the same quartzite in Brittany today. This was a braided river that periodically spilt over its banks, depositing its load onto the floodplain.

It seems the river stopped flowing quite suddenly, the junction with the Otter Sandstone above is abrupt. If you look carefully at the junction you will note the presence of angular pebbles, indicative of erosion by wind rather than water; we have a change to dry, arid conditions. This did not last long however, the Otter Sandstone above was again deposited by seasonal rivers flowing across the desert landscape.

Today the pebbles and the sand that binds them are once more being eroded by water and many will no doubt be included in future sedimentary layers.

Main picture: The Budleigh Salterton Pebble Bed with, near the top of the picture, the sharp junction with the Otter Sandstone above it.

Left: The beach at Budleigh Salterton. The pebble bed is at the bottom of the cliffs at the far end of the beach.

Ladram Bay ~ *mighty stacks*

The well known beauty spot of Ladram Bay has been cut into the relatively soft Otter Sandstone of the Triassic Period. These layers were deposited by fast flowing, braided rivers on a wide flood plain. In the desert environment the rivers would probably have been seasonal, originating in mountains to the south. The rock stacks in the bay are part of its charm and are the result of a chance combination of circumstances. This is perhaps no surprise since we don't see such features elsewhere on this part of the coast.

Stacks normally form in more resistant rocks, like the Chalk of the famous Old Harry stack between Swanage and Studland, and

the limestone of Durdle Door (which will relatively soon become a stack!). At Ladram Bay, the stacks are protected somewhat by a hard sandstone layer at the base. This layer dips gently to the east, so east and west of the bay the layer is respectively lower or higher in the sequence - hence stacks have not formed there. Local structural weaknesses have also been important and erosion has happened more quickly along the near vertical joints in the sandstones (see also Durdle Door page 74). This is also a fairly low energy site in terms of wave power. All in all, Ladram Bay serves as a fine reminder that the shape of coastlines is strongly controlled by the type of rock present and the structural features of those rocks.

The small picture shows the view north-eastwards from Ladram Bay. Notice how the angle of the tall cliff changes about half way up – here the Otter Sandstone gives way to the Mercia Mudstone above it. This formation consists of muds, silts and occasionally evaporite deposits laid down in a different environment to that of the Otter Sandstone. The rivers had retreated southwards and been replaced by an environment of mudflats with seasonal, often hypersaline lakes. Flash floods resulted in more rapid deposition and salt and gypsum precipitated out when the lakes dried up. Occasional dry periods saw the deposition of wind blown sands and silts.

Main picture: Stacks of Otter Sandstone at Ladram Bay.
Left: A view from Ladram Bay to High Peak. Notice the change in angle of the cliff representing the change to the Mercia Mudstone.

Hooken Cliff ~ *a major landslide*

Some may think they spoil a beautiful coastline but landslips played a significant part in the Jurassic Coast becoming a World Heritage Site. Every year thousands more fossils tumble from the cliffs and are eagerly sought by enthusiastic amateur and professional collectors. These fossils have contributed enormously to our understanding of the evolution of life in the Mesozoic Era. The reason why there are so many landslips along the Jurassic Coast is not hard to understand. There are often permeable layers of rock, in particular the Chalk and limestones, overlying impermeable layers, clays and mudstones. As water soaks through the permeable rock it creates a lubricated layer where it reaches the impermeable strata. If the strata dip seawards, at some stage there will almost inevitably be a landslip.

This is exactly what happened one night at Hooken Cliff in March 1790. Here the permeable Chalk with Upper Greensand limestone beneath it rests on Triassic mudstones, all dipping gently out to sea. A huge section of Chalk slipped extending the shoreline by nearly two hundred metres. It is estimated that between seven and ten acres of coastline fell about two hundred metres. Before the fall a huge fissure had opened up behind the cliff edge. A couple of years previously, a small stream that emerged about half way down the original cliff face had stopped flowing, presumably because of some sort of blockage. This may have caused the water to spread out and form a well lubricated layer between the limestone and the mudstone, eventually leading to the massive landslide.

Today Hooken Cliff is one of the more picturesque landslip sites; vegetation has grown over the slipped Chalk creating a sort of "lost world" feel along the path that meanders down through it, and the view from the top is certainly impressive.

Main picture: Looking west from the cliff top across the Hooken landslip.

Left: A close up of "The Pinnacles". Notice to the west that the Chalk sits on top of the red Triassic sandstones. This is the "Great Unconformity" and the Jurassic rocks are completely missing here (see page 96 for explanation of "unconformity"). Note also that the Chalk is thinner here than elsewhere; this may indicate that the depth of the ancient Chalk sea was controlled by fault lines.

The Jurassic Coast World Heritage Site

The Jurassic Coast was awarded World Heritage Site status by UNESCO in 2001; the first natural site in England to achieve this. The award was in recognition of the fact that this stretch of coastline offers a unique "walk through time" of 185 million years of Earth's history, from around 250 to 65 million years ago. From it we can learn much about the processes that have formed the rocks and shaped the coastline, and about the evolution of life in this important era of geological time.

The rocks of the Jurassic Coast span the entire Mesozoic Era, the Triassic, Jurassic and Cretaceous periods. At the end of the previous Palaeozoic Era, life had been devastated by a mass extinction, the cause of which is still a matter of debate. It may be that intense volcanic activity drastically altered a climate that was already extreme because all the world's landmass was incorporated in the supercontinent of Pangaea. As Pangaea began to break up in the Triassic Period, life recovered and began to flourish again. By the Jurassic land and sea were teeming with a tremendous variety of species, dinosaurs dominated the land and giant reptiles the sea. At the end of the Cretaceous Period came another mass extinction, this time probably caused by a meteorite impact.

These Mesozoic sediments were mostly formed in the shallow seas that were created as the movement of the plates broke up the supercontinent. Land was seldom far away and some rocks, such as the Purbeck limestones, were formed in coastal lagoons where dinosaurs waded through dense forests and swamps. Thus it is that these rocks contain a fantastic collection of fossils which have enabled palaeontologists to piece together the story of the evolution of life in this era. The processes that are eroding the coast constantly reveal more fossils for the professional and amateur alike.

Main picture: Looking westwards along the Jurassic Coast from Swyre Head on the Isle of Purbeck. In the middle of the picture is Kimmeridge Bay while beyond is the precipitous Gad Cliff, topped by Purbeck and Portland limestone.

Left: Chesil Beach, an eighteen mile long storm beach, only formed in its present state around five or six thousand years ago.

Dorset

With no motorways or a city, Dorset is regarded by many as the archetypal rural English county. Its diverse beauty is a product of its geology and the natural and human processes that have shaped it. Almost all of its coastline is included in the Jurassic Coast World Heritage Site and inland there are hills and escarpments of Chalk and mellow Jurassic limestones, and rich, fertile vales of softer sands and clays.

The rocks of Dorset range in age from the Jurassic Period to the Eocene Period of the Cenozoic and are of entirely sedimentary origin – there are no volcanic rocks in the county. In Dorset the rocks have not been contorted into tight folds or been sheared by major thrusts, but still the movement of the plates has been a dominant factor in shaping the landscape. The sediments typically lie in flat or gently dipping strata, many of them deposited in shallow or relatively shallow seas that once covered a much greater area than the present extent of their sediments reveal. The Early Jurassic ocean covered much of what is now Devon and Cornwall, but its sediments deposited there have been eroded away. Towards the end of the Cretaceous the Chalk sea again covered much of southern England, but the Chalk, too, has been eroded from many places.

Following the Cretaceous Britain was uplifted and subject to erosion. The Alpine Orogeny had begun and the Cenozoic rocks that we find in north-east Dorset are typically sands and clays of both marine and non-marine origin, indicating that the sea level was fluctuating due to the continued tectonic activity. These rocks are well displayed on the coast around Poole and Bournemouth.

Main picture: Eggardon Hill is composed of hard Cretaceous rocks, mostly sands and grits, deposited in what was to become the Chalk sea, resting unconformably on Jurassic clays and sands which form the fertile lowland.

Left: Looking over Christchurch Harbour from Hengistbury Head. The headland is made of sands and clays from the Eocene Period of the Cenozoic. These sands and clays also underlie the harbour and form the coast to the west at Bournemouth and to the east around Highcliffe and Barton.

Monmouth Beach ~ *the ammonite graveyard*

The dark shales and limestones that make up the cliffs of Lyme Regis were deposited in Lower Jurassic seas that had recently formed as the supercontinent of Pangaea began to break up. These layers contain an abundance of fossils, reflecting the fact that life had recovered and flourished after the great Permian extinction. Because land was nearby, not only fossils of marine creatures are found but also occasionally flying reptiles that had perhaps wandered a bit too far out to sea.

The relative abundance of different fossils tells us much about the ancient ecosystem in which they lived. The many thousands of ammonites discovered each year were part of the diet of some of the large marine reptiles like the ichthyosaur and

the pliosaur whose fossils are consequently rarer. Many people come to Lyme Regis and neighbouring Charmouth to search for fossils among the slumped remains of cliff falls which continually reveal new finds. If you do, please follow local advice and safety precautions; and if possible join an organised fossil hunt.

Something not to be missed on a visit to Lyme Regis is the "ammonite graveyard". This can be found at the western end of Monmouth Beach (the one west of the Cobb) and is only accessible at low tide, so check beforehand. Here you will find the fossilised remains of hundreds of ammonites of all sizes lying in a horizontal band of hard limestone. Although common elsewhere along the beach, here they seem to have been crammed in. Such layers containing large numbers of fossils can be found in many places in the geological succession and may indicate a sudden change in the ancient environment which led to the death of a large number of animals. You must not attempt to extract the fossils here but it's an ideal place to "collect" with your camera.

Main picture: The "ammonite graveyard" at Lyme Regis. Hundreds of ammonites of all sizes lie in this layer of grey limestone. Other fossils such as bivalves are also visible.
Left: A cluster of ammonites with a twenty pence coin for scale. On some specimens you can see the actual shell material around two hundred million years old. Ammonites swam vertically through the ocean, controlling their depth by pumping gas in and out of the chambers in their shells.

West Bay ~ *golden sandstones*

The towering golden sandstone cliffs east of the harbour at West Bay have long been a favourite with photographers. At the time of writing they have gained fame as the setting for the TV drama "Broadchurch". These Bridport Sands are from the Middle Jurassic and it is thought they were deposited in a large river delta that gradually built from the north into the Jurassic sea. This is supported by the fact that the sands get older as we go northwards. In many of the fallen blocks at the foot of the cliff it is possible to see fossilised worm burrows, confirming that the sandstone had an origin in shallow water.

A striking feature of the cliff are the many harder bands that stick out; clearly more resistant to weathering than the softer sands in between. These are layers that have been cemented by calcium carbonate that precipitated out as the sediment collected. This calcium carbonate came from the shells of marine creatures and it has been proposed that the harder layers represent times when there was relatively little detritus being deposited. Furthermore, a look at the cliffs suggests this alternating pattern happened in a fairly rhythmical way which in turn suggests some sort of rhythmical process. One explanation is that it may be linked to the climate changes occurring as a result of the variation in the tilt of the Earth's axis.

It may come as a surprise to learn that the golden colour is only surface deep. The rock is actually blue/grey in colour and it is only the oxidation of the iron content on exposure to the atmosphere that gives the rock its golden appearance.

The Bridport Sands continue in the cliffs at Burton Beach but are not to be seen east of here or west of the harbour at West Bay. Why is this when the strata seem to lie horizontally? The answer lies in faults which have moved strata vertically – east of Burton Beach for example the Bridport Sands lie buried underneath younger Jurassic sediments which have been shifted down.

Main picture: East Cliff seen from the Jurassic Pier, West Bay.

Left: The Bridport Sands at Burton Beach. Again, the harder bands cemented by calcium carbonate are clearly visible. Note how the sea is eroding a notch at the base of the cliff.

Clavell's Hard ~ *the Kimmeridge Clay*

The Kimmeridge Clay Formation comprises a group of shales, mudstones and limestones from the Upper Jurassic around 150 million years ago. The dark grey colour of these sediments is an indication of the high organic content of the strata, around 3.8% at Kimmeridge, the locality which gives this formation its name. In fact the Kimmeridge Clay extends from Dorset through to Lincolnshire and out into the North Sea. At Kimmeridge it is around five hundred metres thick, much of this below beach level. It was deposited in a warm, tropical and relatively shallow sea where the bottom was oxygen poor – hence the high organic content. This may have been due to the nature of the circulation within this ancient sea. Where the strata are deeply buried under the North Sea the pressure and temperature have allowed the formation of oil and natural gas from the organic remains.

The Kimmeridge Clay is not all clay but consists of alternate bands of clay, shale and limestone. One of the layers is a band of hard, bituminous shale which has, over the centuries, been the focus of attempts at economic exploitation. Iron Age people cut and polished it to make jewellery, finding it a very passable substitute for jet. From the seventeenth century it was used in a number of enterprises as fuel; local people had long burnt it instead of coal. In the mid nineteenth century largely unsuccessful attempts were made to process it and produce the substances usually distilled from coal; paraffin, grease and pitch.

The warm seas in which these rocks were deposited were inhabited by many creatures and their remains lie buried in the strata. A quick walk along the shore at Kimmeridge will reveal dozens of ammonites lying on ancient sea floors. The skeletons of wonderful marine reptiles – ichthyosaurs, pliosaurs and plesiosaurs – have also been found in the Kimmeridge Clay, and at the time of writing work has begun on a new museum at Kimmeridge to house the fossil collection of local resident and world famous fossil collector, Steve Etches. When finished it will be well worth a visit.

Main picture: Clavell's Hard is the small promontory in the bottom left of the picture. This is where the oil shale was mined in the nineteenth century.
Left: Kimmeridge Bay - the blocks are from layers of limestone within the sequence which form the dangerous Kimmeridge ledges out to sea.

Portland Bill ~ *the best building stone*

Portland Stone has been quarried on the Isle of Portland since Roman times, but large scale extraction really began in the seventeenth century with the rebuilding of London after the Great Fire and in particular Sir Christopher Wren's choice of the stone for the new St Paul's Cathedral. It reached a zenith in the nineteenth century with the coming of the railway, meaning the stone could be transported more easily inland. Previously it had largely been exported by ship; the gentle southerly dip of the strata had greatly facilitated the quarrying and loading of stone on the southern side of the isle.

Why is Portland Stone such a good material for monumental buildings? Firstly it possesses great strength and this is partly due to the high proportion of calcium carbonate it contains, around

ninety-five per cent. Another reason is that it occurs in thick, homogeneous layers that can be split and cut into large blocks. Thick layers in sediments represent long periods of stable conditions and/or relatively rapid deposition; it is changing conditions that result in layers of different composition. Much of Portland Stone is what is known as "oolitic" limestone, a term derived from the Greek word oon meaning egg, and so called because the texture of the rock resembles fish roe, with tiny spherical "ooids" cemented together. On the floor of a shallow tropical sea minute sand grains or shell fragments were rolled backwards and forwards by the action of the waves and tides. As they rolled around calcium carbonate from the supersaturated sea water precipitated around them, the rolling action first exposing one side then the other, resulting in concentric layers of calcium carbonate. The texture can just be seen with the naked eye on a freshly broken rock sample. It is thought that such sediments are today forming off the coast of the Bahamas where oolitic sand can be found on the beaches. The ooids are cemented together after deposition by the precipitation of calcium carbonate from groundwater.

Main picture: The lighthouse at Portland Bill and the quarried layers of Portland Stone. In a number of places the limestone is crammed with fossils of oysters, a further indication that it was formed in very shallow waters.

Left: More quarried ledges on the shore with, in the background, an old "whim" used to lower blocks of stone onto boats.

White Nothe ~ *what is chalk?*

Chalk is a familiar yet mysterious sedimentary rock. In its pure form it is almost entirely organic, formed from the remains of tiny creatures that still inhabit the warm, upper waters of tropical oceans in countless numbers. The mystery is why there is no sand, silt or mud in the rock – or very little. Did the Chalk accumulate in water far from any land where no terrestrial sediment could reach or did it form in oceans surrounded by waterless deserts where there were no rivers to bring eroded sediment? These are two explanations that have been offered.

Whatever the reason there is no doubt that chalk is a marine sediment that accumulated in a warm, tropical ocean, probably no more than three hundred metres deep. This sea was teeming with life and at the bottom of the food chain were microscopic photosynthesising organisms that need to be present in vast numbers if larger animals are to prosper. One such organism is a type of phytoplankton known as a coccolithophore. This tiny creature protects itself with plates of calcium carbonate, up to thirty of them, each typically three thousandths of a millimetre in diameter. They are beautifully crafted with intricate designs. The plates are constantly being replaced and discarded ones sink to the bottom – in places ocean waters are milky white due to the billions of these plates (coccoliths). It is staggering to think that the gradual accumulation of these tiny, delicate shields has formed rock hundreds of feet thick, even more so when you realise that the original sediment has been compressed by the gradually increasing load by a factor as much as ten.

Chalk is not made entirely of coccoliths however, the shells of foraminifera are also present in great numbers. These are tiny amoeboid creatures, some of which dwelt on the ocean bottom while some were planktonic. Their shells, too, are wonderfully intricate and much bigger than the plates of the coccolithophores, up to a millimetre in diameter.

Main picture: Looking eastwards along the spectacular Chalk cliffs from White Nothe.
Left: Looking westwards towards Weymouth. Note the landslips in the bottom half of the photograph.

Lulworth Cove ~ *a fossil forest*

Few places are more visited by school field trips than Lulworth. The formation of this uniquely beautiful circular cove is easy to appreciate in principle – the sea has broken through the hard, vertically dipping outer limestone layers that trend parallel to the coast and has eroded away the softer sands and clays behind, before coming up against another more resistant rock, the Chalk. All the rocks here dip vertically or nearly so and the explanation for this structure is told elsewhere (see page 84).

Why did the sea break through the limestone barrier here? Was it the sea that originally broke through? It is now thought that the river flowing into the cove through the village played a major part. At the end of the Ice Age it would have been swollen with meltwater and probably found its way to the sea by eroding a gap in the Portland and Purbeck limestones. Rising sea levels would have widened the breach and enabled the sea to begin eroding the softer strata behind.

Lulworth is also famous for the Fossil Forest, perched on the cliffs to the east of the cove and only accessible when the army ranges are open (most weekends and main school holidays). Some may be disappointed that there are no trunks of petrified wood here but the remains are fascinating nonetheless. What you see are the fossilised remains of algal growths known as stromatolites around the bases and trunks of rotting trees. These trees, mainly a variety of cypress, once flourished around the edge of coastal swamps and lagoons in the Late Jurassic. Dinosaurs would have lumbered past, munching on their leaves. The area was subject to variations in sea level and it is thought that a rise in sea level and consequent increase in salinity may have killed these trees.

Main picture: Lulworth Cove. The entrance to the cove is flanked by the steeply dipping Portland and Purbeck limestones, here much thinner than further east on the Purbeck coast. In between the limestones and the Chalk at the back of the cove are Cretaceous soft sands and clays, chiefly of the Wealden Series. These and the Chalk are also steeply dipping.

Left: Stromatolites in the Fossil Forest. One shows growth around a circular tree stump, another around a fallen trunk.

Durdle Door ~ *a natural arch*

Durdle Door is a natural arch composed of Portland and Purbeck limestones. At this part of the coast the strata are dipping almost vertically (including the Chalk to the north) and are part of a large fold known as the Purbeck Monocline (see page 84). This is a large scale feature; several miles to the south-east, on the coast of the Isle of Purbeck, the Portland and Purbeck limestones are dipping gently southwards, part of the horizontal limb of the monocline.

On the arch the harder Portland limestone faces the sea to the south with the younger Purbeck rocks directly behind it landwards. Once the erosive power of the sea had penetrated the Portland layers, it quickly eroded the softer Purbeck rocks behind, forming caves and later arches as the erosion continued. An earlier coastline can be traced by the isolated stacks of Portland limestone sticking above the waves to the west of Durdle Door and to the east in Man O' War Bay. One day the arch of Durdle Door will collapse and another stack will have been formed, eventually also to disappear.

Joints in the rocks play an important part in their erosion. Air in joints is compressed by the weight of water as it surges, creating considerable hydraulic pressure in the joints, weakening the rocks and leading to their eventual collapse. Joints such as these are fractures in brittle strata caused by tensional stresses in the rocks, often associated with folding. Faults, too, can be caused by tension but also demonstrate some vertical or horizontal displacement along the plane of the fault. Look closely at the arch of Durdle Door and you will see the "blocky" appearance of the limestones due to its erosion being dominated by two sets of joints.

Main picture: The limestone arch of Durdle Door. To the left of the arch the low, slumped strata are the Cretaceous sands and clays of the Wealden Series.

Left: To the west of Durdle Door we see a wave cut platform eroded by the sea in the Chalk.

Man O' War Bay ~ *a concordant coastline*

In April 2013 a huge section of the Chalk cliffs of Man O' War Bay collapsed onto the beach and sea below. Chalk is soluble and is quite rapidly dissolved by seawater; in places erosion of chalk cliffs is at the rate of around half a metre a year. Here in Man O' War Bay and neighbouring St Oswald's Bay the Chalk is dipping almost vertically, meaning that the bedding planes of the different layers which are the main planes of weakness are also nearly vertical. At times the water in the bay was milky white, a powerful reminder of the ongoing recycling of the crust – the calcium carbonate returned to the seawater may someday eventually become part of another sedimentary rock, perhaps next time a limestone. Some may be incorporated into the shells of sea creatures which become fossils discovered by future palaeontologists.

The coastline here is said to be "concordant", that is the different strata run parallel to the coast. A "discordant" coastline has strata that are at a high angle to the direction of the shore. The features we see in this area are typical of a concordant coastline. A relatively thin band of Portland and Purbeck limestones once formed the first line of defence from the sea and where this has been breached the sea has eroded the softer rocks behind, scooping out bays like Lulworth Cove and Man O' War Bay. The almost vertically dipping limestones can be seen forming rocky outcrops at the edge of the bay and continue westwards to form the arch at Durdle Door and eastwards the entrance to Lulworth Cove. You might note also that eastwards from Durdle Door the bays and coves on the coast become larger as the thickness of the softer sediments between the limestones and the Chalk increases, while the dip of the strata decreases.

Main picture: Man O' War Bay. The steeply dipping Purbeck and Portland limestones can be seen forming a line across the bay and appearing above the water again at the far end of St Oswald's Bay.
Left: Worbarrow Bay, east of Lulworth and Durdle Door. The Portland and Purbeck beds are dipping less steeply (middle left of picture) while the bay is carved out of the much thicker soft sediments sandwiched between the Chalk at the far end of the bay and the limestones.

Sherborne Abbey ~ *golden Jurassic limestone*

Limestone is a sedimentary rock that contains a large proportion of calcium carbonate, usually in the form of the mineral calcite. It is thought that around ten per cent in volume of the Earth's sedimentary rock is limestone. The calcium carbonate comes from the remains of creatures that use it to build their hard parts. Most limestone is formed from skeletal fragments of marine organisms such as coral and foraminifera, and larger organisms like molluscs and brachiopods. It is often cemented by the precipitation of calcite or aragonite which forms coatings around the fragments and in interstitial spaces. The solubility of calcium carbonate increases with pressure, decreasing temperature and increased carbon dioxide; this effectively restricts the formation of limestone to relatively shallow marine environments. How do we get from a soft, calcium carbonate mud at the bottom of the sea to a hard crystalline rock? The answer is basically by compression. As the bits of calcium carbonate are squeezed they dissolve around the points of contact. This dissolved calcium carbonate then migrates to the spaces between the grains where it precipitates again due to there being less pressure. The grains become cemented together.

By the Early Jurassic, sea had spread across most of England although Cornwall and much of Devon was still land. To the north was the Scottish Landmass and to the east what has been called the Anglo-Brabant Landmass. We can picture a warm, shallow sea between these areas of land, teeming with life. It is in this sea that Ham Stone was formed, so called after Ham Hill in Somerset, where it has been quarried since ancient times. Ham Stone is a medium to coarse grained shelly limestone that has been well cemented by crystalline calcite. Its rich golden colour is due to the presence of grains of the mineral goethite or iron hydroxide which precipitated as the rock was forming, a process known as diagenesis.

Ham Stone has been used to build many prominent buildings in north Dorset and Somerset, including the magnificent abbey at Sherborne, most of which dates from the fifteenth century, including the wonderful fan vaulting pictured.

Main picture: The fan vaulting in the nave of Sherborne Abbey.

Left: Sherborne Abbey, built of Ham Stone.

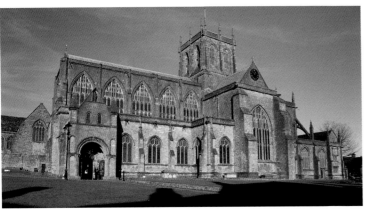

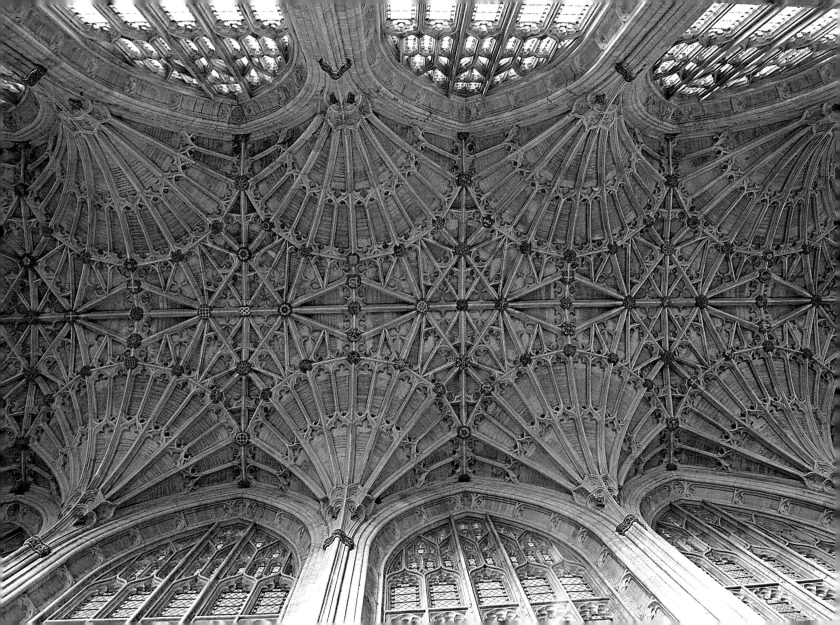

Houns-tout ~ *changing environments*

Houns-tout cliff stands one hundred and forty metres or about four hundred and fifty feet above Chapman's Pool at the western end of the Isle of Purbeck. "Tout" is related to an Old English word meaning to peer or look out, and the view along the Jurassic Coast will not disappoint. The cliff owes its impressive height to the top layers of Portland and Purbeck limestone, which here lie horizontally.

The building up of the geological history of an area is a complicated business, but exposures such as Houns-tout are extremely useful: in this cliff is a record of the environments of much of the Late Jurassic and the beginning of the Cretaceous Period. At the foot of the cliff we have the Kimmeridge Clay, not all clay, but shales, mudstones and thin bands of limestones. These rocks were deposited in a relatively shallow tropical sea, probably some sort of basin where inflow and outflow was restricted, resulting in a sea floor with little oxygen; hence the high organic content of the strata.

As we progress up the cliff, later in the time scale, conditions change and we find the lighter coloured rocks of the Portland Sand series. These rocks have little organic content and we have clearly moved out of the restricted basin of the Kimmeridge Clay. Although called the Portland Sand Formation, the layers are mostly clays or marls. Marl is clay with a large calcium carbonate content and it is known that this can form where there are large numbers of photosynthesising algae. The presence of some fine grained sandstones indicates a shallowing of the Jurassic sea and these strata may have been formed in a warm, shallow, algae rich ocean.

Still further up the cliff we have the Portland Stone, a limestone formed in a shallow tropical sea, rich in life, while at the very top lies the Purbeck limestone, deposited in shallow, coastal lagoons, often in brackish water. We know this from the fossils of molluscs found there, species which today inhabit fresh or brackish water. We also find plant remains and occasionally dinosaur footprints, a clear sign that we are not looking at an ocean floor here!

Main picture: Houns-tout cliff capped by Portland and Purbeck limestones with the Portland Sand and Kimmeridge Clay beneath.
Left: A view from St Aldhelm's Head to Houns-tout.

Hambledon Hill ~ *the edge of the Chalk*

The Chalk upland dominates central Dorset and the escarpment on its northern and western edge provides many fine viewpoints over the Vale of Blackmore. Hambledon Hill is at the north-western edge and separated from the main line of the escarpment by the River Stour to the west and the River Iwerne to the east. It is separated from its neighbouring hillfort of Hod Hill by a dry valley to the south. Many dry valleys cut the Chalk escarpment and it may seem odd that this is so – chalk is permeable and water only flows on the surface where the water table lies at ground level. However, during the Ice Age, although not covered by an ice sheet, southern Britain experienced permafrost, and in the

short summers meltwater rivers flowed over the frozen ground and carved the valleys we now see on the Chalk.

The Chalk sea once covered much of western Europe and lasted from about 100 million years ago to around 75 million years ago. Chalk originally extended further west but has been eroded exposing the older strata beneath; to the east it can be found under the younger Tertiary deposits of the Hampshire Basin. Older Jurassic strata had been subjected to millions of years of erosion before the sea returned in the Cretaceous and marine sediments were laid down, culminating in the Chalk. The valley of the River Stour to the west of Hambledon Hill is underlain by Kimmeridge and Oxford clays from the Late Jurassic. At this time the southern British Isles saw the creation of several marine basins separated by ridges of land. In these subsiding basins circulation was restricted and the sea floor was consequently poor in oxygen. Thick layers of organic-rich mudstones accumulated, later becoming the source rocks for the extensive North Sea oilfields.

Hambledon Hill was an important site in Neolithic times, when a causewayed camp was situated here and continued to be used until the Iron Age when a major hillfort was built.

Main picture: The north-west corner of Hambledon Hill showing the Iron Age ramparts cut into the side of the hill. Beyond is the rich agricultural land of the Vale of Blackmore, underlain by Jurassic clays but also some limestones.

Left: Looking west towards the River Stour from Hambledon Hill.

Corfe Castle ~ *the Purbeck Monocline*

Corfe Castle sits in a natural gap in the Purbeck Hills, an obvious and sensible place for a defensive structure. The Normans first built a stone castle here but there was an earlier wooden Saxon stronghold providing an important barrier to Viking raiders coming inland from the coast. The hills are formed from a narrow band of Chalk running roughly east-west; narrow because here the Chalk strata are dipping almost vertically, so the width of the ridge represents the thickness of the Chalk layers. We have seen the vertically dipping Chalk strata before on the coast at Man O' War Bay and noted that tremendous forces must have been involved in tilting the originally flat layers. In fact the Chalk ridge is part of what is known as the Purbeck Monocline, a large fold formed on the edge of the Alpine Orogeny about 30 million years ago.

The Chalk itself is around 65 million years old and the Jurassic sediments which are also folded are more than 100 million years old. These rocks had lain buried, undisturbed for many millions of years before they were contorted by huge earth movements.

A monocline is a step-like fold with one vertical and one horizontal limb; in Purbeck these are represented by the steeply dipping Chalk and on the southern part of the isle by the horizontal Portland and Purbeck limestones. Note also the limestones are almost vertical at Lulworth Cove and Man O' War Bay. It has been stated that the Purbeck Monocline represents a ripple on the edge of the great mountain building episode that formed the Alps; but how is it that such forces can be transmitted through the crust many hundreds of miles from the centre of the folding? The sedimentary rocks that we see on the surface of the crust lie on an older "basement" of harder igneous and metamorphic rocks and it is through these that it is thought stresses and strains are transmitted, sometimes resulting in the deformation of the less "competent" sedimentary cover above.

Main picture: Corfe Castle sits on an isolated hill in the Chalk ridge. This has been created by two streams either side of the castle which flowed northwards across the Chalk. It is unusual for streams to cut across the prevailing structure like this and probably occurred after the English Channel had been uplifted by the Alpine earth movements.
Left: Handfast Point and Old Harry Rocks, the end of the Chalk and the Jurassic Coast.

Somerset

Somerset is a diverse county both in terms of landscape and geology. Apart from a very small extent of Silurian volcanic deposits, the rocks of Somerset date from the Devonian to the Cretaceous periods and are all sedimentary. It should be said that there are younger deposits from the Pleistocene or Ice Age when meltwater rivers and higher sea levels left silts, sands and gravels at a number of places.

The Devonian sediments form the high ground of the Quantocks, Brendon Hills and Exmoor. These were deposited in the ocean to the south of the great Old Red Sandstone continent, weathered from the mountains that the Caledonian Orogeny had created. They were to be caught up in another mountain building episode at the end of the Carboniferous Period. As a result the rocks are often hard, having been baked and compressed by the earth movements – sandstones often turn into quartzites by such treatment, the quartz grains fusing together under the heat and pressure. No wonder these rocks form high ground.

The sea was much more widespread over Britain during the Carboniferous and limestone from this period today forms the Mendip Hills. In the Permian and Triassic periods Somerset, like the rest of Britain, was part of the supercontinent of Pangaea and seasonal rivers and lakes were responsible for the bulk of sediments from this age, alongside wind blown desert sands. The sea returned during the Jurassic depositing thick sequences of clays and limestones. Another period of uplift and erosion was followed by the Chalk sea in the Cretaceous. More tectonic activity raised the area again above sea level since when continued erosion has left the Somerset we see today.

Geological history has been kind to Somerset providing it with a rich collection of limestones, from the hard, grey Carboniferous variety with numerous economic uses to the wonderfully coloured Jurassic ones used for building stone.

Main picture: A view from Ham Hill over the Somerset Levels. The honey coloured Ham Stone has been quarried here for many years and was used in many local buildings (see page 78).
Below: Wells Cathedral built from Doulting Stone, another of Somerset's Jurassic limestones, used for building since Roman times.

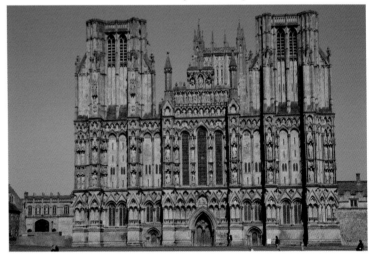

Glastonbury Tor ~ *mysterious outlier*

———————

A lot has been written about Glastonbury Tor, much of it concerning myths and legends. An aura of mystery has grown up around it which extends to its physical nature. It has been claimed that the hill is largely hollow or contains a multitude of waterways and that it is a magnetic power point or centre of cosmic energy. But whether or not it was ever part of an Arthurian world or held the Holy Grail, we can know some things for sure about it.

Glastonbury Tor is a classic example of an outlier, a hill that has been left isolated by the erosion of strata around it. Its subsequent relative resistance has been provided by a hard cap of Bridport Sand, a rock that we have met before at West Bay. Below this are more Jurassic layers, a limestone known as the Junction Bed, a sandy mudstone called the Upper Dyrham Formation and then the Pennard Sand followed by more mudstones of the Lower Dyrham Formation. You might have guessed by the names and descriptions that some of these rocks are permeable while some are not, a perfect recipe for springs. The Junction Bed and Pennard Sand are important aquifers and collect water from a significant area north of the Tor. Around the Tor a number of springs discharge from the bottom of the Pennard Sand where it meets the impermeable mudstones below.

Faults can play an important part in the movement of groundwater; if an impermeable layer is downthrown against a permeable rock, the movement of water may be impeded and a spring might result. This is what has happened at the Chalice Well where the Pennard Sand has been downthrown against the mudstones of the Lower Dyrham Formation. Again, many myths have grown up around this spring, particularly about its healing powers. It is a chalybeate spring, containing a significant proportion of dissolved ferrous iron. Where it discharges a deposit of red iron hydroxide is formed.

Main picture: Glastonbury Tor with St Michael's Tower on its top. Note the terraces on the side of the hill. There are seven of these and their origin is still something of a mystery. They do not seem to be agricultural terraces (strip lynchets) as they are equally developed on the north side of the hill. It has been suggested that they represent a three dimensional labyrinth and had some sort of ritual purpose.
Left: The iron rich water of the Chalice Well.

Ebbor Gorge ~ *no mini-Cheddar*

Somerset's Mendip Hills are composed of Carboniferous limestone, laid down in a warm, tropical sea around three hundred and fifty million years ago. This sea was extensive and the limestone is also found across large areas of northern England as well as the Avon Gorge near Bristol. Look at an Ordnance Survey map of the Mendips and you will see no rivers flowing across it but a number of streams issuing from its edges where the limestone gives way to other rock types. This is easily explained by the fact that the limestone is permeable, water soaks through it, aided by the many vertical joints, dissolving underground cave systems and

perhaps reaching the surface when it encounters an impermeable rock. The erosional features of limestone uplands like the Mendips and the Yorkshire Dales are usually things like sink holes and the clints and dykes of limestone pavement. How is it then that on the edge of the Mendips we see deep gorges that are typical of erosion by powerful watercourses?

Ebbor Gorge is less well known than its neighbour Cheddar but equally beautiful. Cut into the south-west side of the Mendips, its more intimate character gives the visitor a sense of discovery as well as breathtaking views and abundant wildlife to admire. The gorge is thought to have been formed by summer meltwater from the snows of the last ice age. Permafrost would have ensured that the ground was impermeable and torrential streams and rivers would have eroded into the surface. A similar process was responsible for the dry valleys of Dorset's Chalk uplands (see page 82). Ebbor is not just a steep river valley however, it is a deeply incised gorge with, at its head, a classic example of a "nick point". This is a point where a river has suddenly become more powerful and begun eroding downwards more forcefully; it is characteristic of "rejuvenation" caused by a relatively sudden increase in the river's gradient, probably as a result of a colder period during the Ice Age when the sea level would have dropped (see also page 30).

Main picture: Ebbor Gorge from the top looking over the Somerset Levels.
Left: A view of the "nick point" at the head of the gorge.

Watchet ~ *alabaster*

For geologists the little town of Watchet on the Bristol Channel is every bit as important as Lyme Regis. The rocks here date from the Triassic when desert conditions dominated and seasonal lakes gradually filled with sediment, and the Lower Jurassic (or Lias) whose dark, marine clays contain the fossils of ammonites and early reptiles.

The cliffs contain large deposits of fine grained translucent gypsum, often known as alabaster. This was much prized by sculptors in the seventeenth century as an alternative to marble. It is a soft mineral and therefore easy to work, but only suitable for indoor decorative purposes. A thriving industry developed exporting it from the small harbour. Gypsum is hydrated calcium sulphate, it formed in the unhydrated form anhydrite as an evaporite deposit in the temporary lakes of the arid Triassic Period. Evaporites are the inevitable products of such environments and much common salt is extracted from ancient desert sediments. At Watchet we see not only layers and nodules of gypsum as we would expect, but also fine, intricate connected veins of the mineral. For a mineral vein to form the mineral must first be a fluid; there has to be a source of the mineral, fractures for the fluid to move through and finally the right conditions for precipitation.

At Watchet it is thought the stresses and strains associated with the Alpine mountain building episode were the driving factors behind the formation of the gypsum veins. The source of the mineral was the layers and nodules that formed as evaporite deposits. Water from deeper levels dissolved the anhydrite as it moved through faults. This increased its volume and the resultant increase in pressure led to fracturing of the rocks. The fluid forced its way along the thin, interconnected fractures and, as the pressure and temperature decreased, precipitated as gypsum.

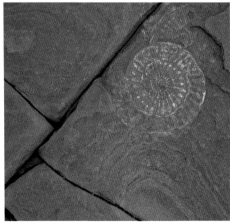

Main picture: Veins of gypsum in the cliffs at Watchet. The veins have also been slightly folded.

Far left: Gypsum nodules in the cliffs at Watchet.

Left: Watchet is also a famous fossil location.

Cadbury Castle ~ *the edge of the Levels*

Isolated hills were often seen by Iron Age folk as good places to build a hillfort and at Cadbury Castle we find one of the most famous of such structures. It has been claimed that it is the site of King Arthur's Camelot, a claim given credence by the discovery that it was re-occupied in the Dark Ages after the Romans had left. Like many such hills, Cadbury was not always isolated; it was once part of the Jurassic escarpment capped by the Inferior Oolite (oolitic limestone, see page 68). The escarpment here made a sharp turn and two streams running perpendicular to each other gradually cut this hill off.

The view from the castle to the west is spectacular, over the fertile plain of the Somerset Levels. Underlying the Levels are mostly Triassic rocks such as the Mercia Mudstones, but on the surface we find much more recent deposits. At the height of the last ice age the sea level was some one hundred and thirty metres below today's level. As the climate warmed and the ice melted it is thought that the sea began to invade the area of the Levels about 8-9000 years ago, creating saltmarsh and mudflats similar to what we find in the intertidal reaches of the Severn Estuary today. As well as clay from these inlets of the sea we also find peat over parts of the Levels, some of it formed in freshwater reed beds where drainage of freshwater had been prevented by the build up of the marine clay. The Levels are now between five and six metres above mean sea level but with a tidal range in the Severn Estuary up to nine metres above mean sea level it can be appreciated that only the presence of coastal defences prevents them returning to saltmarsh and mudflats. Sea walls and river levees were first built by the Romans in an effort to produce more land for agriculture.

The Levels remain in a precarious situation, largely due to the threat of sea level rise brought about by global warming, but also by the continued sinking of southern Britain after the Ice Age as northern Britain "bounces back" following the removal of the ice.

Main picture: Looking north-west from the ramparts of Cadbury Castle over the Somerset Levels. Without artificial sea and river defences the castle would be on the coast and the Levels an inlet of the sea covered by saltmarsh and mudflats.

Left: A view from the northern ramparts of this Iron Age hillfort.

Vallis Vale ~ *a famous geologist*

An old limestone quarry near Frome is something of a place of pilgrimage for geologists. Here is the so called "De la Beche unconformity", so striking a feature that even the untrained eye might recognise it as something unusual. Sir Henry De la Beche (1796-1855) was a pioneer of geology. He spent much of his childhood in Lyme Regis and became interested in geology through his friendship with Mary Anning. He later joined the Geological Society of London and after working with the Ordnance Survey helped set up and became the first director of the Geological Survey of Great Britain. The unconformity at Vallis Vale was described in the world's first geological survey memoir.

An unconformity is a junction between two rock layers that represents a gap in time between their deposition or formation. When looking at sedimentary strata we commonly assume that each layer followed on immediately from the one below, its different appearance indicating changes in the environment of deposition or source of sediment. However, there may have been a considerable time gap between the deposition of the layers, the sediments may have been uplifted and been part of a continental landmass before the sea returned and more sediments were deposited. This will be more obvious if the older layers have been folded or tilted as they were uplifted, so that the younger layers are clearly lying at a different angle. This is exactly what we have at Vallis Vale where the horizontal layers of the Middle Jurassic Inferior Oolite (oolitic limestone, see page 68) lie directly on the steeply dipping layers of the Carboniferous limestone. There is an age difference of around 170-180 million years between these two rock formations! Before the Jurassic rocks were deposited the Carboniferous limestones were part of a landmass that was gradually eroded and inundated as the Jurassic seas transgressed over the old desert landscape of Pangaea, much as the Carboniferous seas had done over a more ancient landscape millions of years before. In nearby quarries that have extracted the hard limestone we see conglomerates overlying the Carboniferous. These are pebbly beach sediments deposited as the sea gradually encroached on the land.

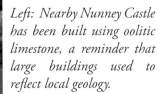

Main picture: The De la Beche unconformity at Vallis Vale is in an old limestone quarry. The hard Carboniferous limestone makes excellent roadstone. The junction between the two limestones is clear.

Left: Nearby Nunney Castle has been built using oolitic limestone, a reminder that large buildings used to reflect local geology.

Cothelstone Hill, the Quantocks ~ *a major fault*

Apart from a few Silurian rocks of limited extent, the oldest rocks in Somerset are Devonian in age. These form the upland regions of Exmoor, the Brendon Hills and the Quantocks. As we have seen, elsewhere in Britain to the north, Devonian rocks are described as the Old Red Sandstone. They are typically red, desert sandstones similar to those of the Permian and Triassic periods we find in Devon which were, and occasionally still are, described as the New Red Sandstone. To the south the Devonian rocks are almost everywhere dark, contorted slates. In the nineteenth century there was great controversy about the dating of these rocks; in many of the strata fossils were rare and it was not easy to correlate the very different layers in different parts of the country. Eventually there was agreement and it was shown that at the same time as desert sandstones were accumulating in the Midlands and North,

turbidity currents (see page 16) were tumbling down a continental submarine slope in Cornwall.

The Devonian rocks of Somerset represent something of a dividing line between these two contrasting ancient geographies. To the north the great Caledonian mountains were being rapidly eroded by fast rivers which in turn carried the detritus to arid floodplains below; while to the south sediments were settling in the marine trough known as the North Variscan Foredeep (see page 38). Somerset was on the dividing line between these two regions and the rocks we see on the Quantocks were formed on and near the coastal plain of the great Old Red Sandstone continent. The oldest of the Devonian rocks of the Quantocks are known by the rather grisly name of the Hangman Grits and among these sandstones and shales are occasional conglomerates, a typical deposit of a shoreline (see page 36). On Cothelstone Hill the rocks visible are from the younger Ilfracombe Series and are mainly sandstones and shales of marine origin. The sandstones are usually very hard, having been "baked" somewhat by the effects of temperature and pressure during the Variscan Orogeny.

Notice that the Devonian of the Quantocks is isolated from that of Exmoor, and separated by a vale of younger, largely Triassic rocks. This is because the younger rocks have been downthrown by a large fault running along the south-western side of the upland.

Main picture: Hard sandstones on Cothelstone Hill.
Left: Dunster and the coastal plain from the edge of Exmoor.

Cheddar Gorge ~ *Carboniferous limestone*

We have come to another gorge for our final location, perhaps the most famous gorge in all of Britain, and one cut into one of the country's most famous rocks, the Carboniferous limestone. We have met this rock before at Ebbor Gorge and Vallis Vale, and it forms the upland of the Mendip Hills. Dating from around 350 million years ago when tropical Carboniferous seas covered a number of different basins separated by ridges of land, it is formed from millions of shell fragments of animals like corals, brachiopods and crinoids, bound together by a cement of calcitic mud. Almost as much as the later Carboniferous strata, the Coal Measures, this rock has been a major factor in Britain's industrial development,

having an important role in iron smelting. Burnt in a blast furnace, it reacts with silica and other acidic oxides to form calcium silicate which can be drawn off as slag. This rocky material would otherwise clog up the furnace. For centuries it has been burnt to make quicklime for agricultural use; it is used to make cement and makes excellent hardcore for road building. It may come as no surprise that the current nature of Cheddar Gorge owes much to quarrying activities as well as geological and geomorphological processes.

You may have guessed that, like Ebbor Gorge, Cheddar has been formed by river erosion over permafrost during the last ice age. In cold periglacial periods meltwater flowed over the frozen ground and ice and mud blocked the caves and caverns that were formed in the warmer interglacial periods. It has been a common misconception that Cheddar Gorge is the result of the collapse of the roof of a former underground cave system, something that has happened in other limestone areas.

Main picture: A cleft in the Carboniferous limestone on the southern rim of Cheddar Gorge.

Left: A view down the gorge from The Pinnacles on the southern rim. The gentle dip of the strata is apparent on the opposite side, as is the effect of extensive quarrying.

Final words

In recent times, geologically speaking, human activities have contributed more and more to the evolution of the landscape. These activities have often reflected and made use of the underlying geology; farming activity and extractive industries are two examples. Dry stone walls are a common feature of much of Britain's farming landscape; a means of building field boundaries that only required local resources and skill. In the Yorkshire Dales the strong, resistant Carboniferous limestone and Millstone Grit provide ideal raw material, as does the golden Jurassic limestone in the Cotswolds, Somerset and Dorset. The layers of these ancient sediments, reflecting changes in the environment of deposition, give the builders stones of convenient size and shape. In Cornwall the material of choice is slate. Although originally a sedimentary rock, the layers have been formed by the orientation of clay minerals at right angles to the enormous pressure resulting from the collision of tectonic plates. This "slaty cleavage" has also led to the rock being particularly suitable for roof tiles.

The photograph opposite shows a dry stone wall in the village of Tintagel, near the famous castle that, too, was built of local slate. The unusual piece of slate in the middle of the photograph has a wonderful story to tell. Its tiny crystals of clay minerals were once weathered from the mighty Caledonian mountains and brought by fast rivers to the sea that covered this part of the world between 350 and 400 million years ago. Fine sediment like clay would have drifted out to the deeper parts of the sea and gradually settled to the bottom. Year by year the sediment accumulated while, all the time, the sea was being squeezed by the collision of the plates, moving together by a few centimetres every year. The clay turned to rock and as the pressure continued the two dimensional "sheet" minerals gradually regrew sideways to the pressure – the slaty cleavage formed. This was not the end of the "suffering" of this rock; you can see that the cleavage has also been folded, indicating a second period of deformation. It is not unusual for geologists to be able to define a number of such episodes in rocks like these; a mountain chain is not created in one act. Finally the rock we see found itself in the core of another mountain belt, which in turn was eroded until it was, once more, exposed to the atmosphere. For the moment, it has escaped a return to the sea!

Further Reading

In my opinion, two of the best popular guides to Britain's geology and geological processes respectively are:
The Hidden Landscape - a journey into the geological past by Richard Fortey, Bodley Head, 2010 and
The Planet in a Pebble - a journey into Earth's deep history by Jan Zalasiewicz, Oxford University Press, 2010

For a more detailed description of the geology of Devon and Cornwall try:
The Geology of Cornwall: and the Isles of Scilly - various, University of Exeter Press, 1998
The Geology of Devon - various, University of Exeter Press, 1982

For a description of Somerset's geology try:
The Geology of Somerset by Peter Hardy, Ex Libris Press, 1999
Somerset Landscapes by Simon Haslett, CreateSpace Independent Publishing Platform, 2010

And for Dorset:
Geology (Discover Dorset) by Paul Ensom, The Dovecote Press, 1998

A number of regional guides are produced by the British Geological Survey. Details are available at www.bgs.ac.uk.

There is lots of information about the geology of the Jurassic Coast on www.jurassiccoast.org. The Jurassic Coast Trust has a number of publications, details of which are also on the website.

Similarly, www.cornish-mining.org.uk has much infomation on the Cornish Mining World Heritage Site, and likewise for the English Riviera Geopark at www.englishrivierageopark.org.uk.

All photographs are by the author.
Front cover: Prussia Cove, Cornwall. Rear cover: Bell Tor, Dartmoor, Devon.
Title page: Bat's Head, Dorset. This page: Stair Hole, Lulworth Cove, Dorset.